# KEEPER

## ALAN GIBBONS

With illustrations by
**Chris Chalik**

Barrington Stoke

First published in 2021 in Great Britain by
Barrington Stoke Ltd
18 Walker Street, Edinburgh, EH3 7LP

www.barringtonstoke.co.uk

Text © 2021 Alan Gibbons
Illustrations © 2021 Chris Chalik

A CIP catalogue record for this book is available
from the British Library upon request

ISBN: 978-1-78112-963-0

Printed by Hussar Books, Poland

# Contents

# Chapter 1
# The Hulk

It isn't easy starting a new school halfway into the year. Most kids who do start late are quiet to begin with. It takes them time to fit in. They sit at the back of the classroom. They stand at the edge of the playground looking lonely and left out.

Not Shane Logan.

I had never met anybody like Shane Logan.

When he started, he hit our school like a wild wind, like a hurricane. He came into our

classroom one Monday morning with our Head
Teacher, Mr Rust. Shane slammed the door
behind him and the whole room shook.

Mr Rust stared at Shane. He didn't like kids
making noise. Shane didn't notice. He just
stood in front of the class with his feet apart
and his arms crossed over his chest, as if he
was waiting for a fight.

"What's up with the Incredible Hulk?" my
mate Danny Osu asked, nodding to Shane.

"Beats me," I said.

Mr Rust looked at Shane again, as if he was
trouble. Shane ignored him.

"This is Shane Logan," Mr Rust said to
our class. "Shane has just moved here from
Yorkshire."

"Leeds," Shane said with a growl in his voice.

"He thinks he's a big grizzly bear," Danny said, shoving me with his elbow.

"He sounds more like an earthquake to me," I told him. "Did you ever hear anybody that loud?"

Our teacher, Mrs Ali, smiled at the new boy.

"Let's all say hello to Shane," she said, then added, "You can sit over there, next to Peter."

Mrs Ali pointed to the empty seat next to me. Shane stared for a moment, then he stomped over and slumped into the chair. The legs scraped on the floor. Mr Rust gave Mrs Ali a sideways look, shrugged and left the room.

Mrs Ali turned back to Shane and smiled again. "We're in the middle of a Maths lesson at the moment," she said. "I'll get you a book at break-time, but for now you can just listen to what we're doing."

Mrs Ali was about to carry on with the Maths lesson when Shane's hand shot up.

"Do I have to stay in at break to get my book?" he asked.

"No, Shane, don't worry," Mrs Ali said. "I'll get the book. You can go out with the rest of the class."

Shane put his hand down, but it was back up a minute later.

"What if I want to write something down in this lesson?" Shane asked. "I need something to write on now."

"You don't need to write anything down for this lesson," Mrs Ali explained again. "But I can give you some paper if you want."

"Can I have a pencil too?" Shane asked. "I haven't got anything to write with."

That made Danny laugh.

Mrs Ali wasn't used to being asked so many questions. Her voice sounded funny when she replied, "All right. I'll get you a pencil and some paper."

She sighed and placed a sheet of paper and a pencil on his desk. Shane looked at us and grinned.

"Pencil and paper is good," he said with a smile.

"I am glad you're happy," Mrs Ali said.

She had to force herself to smile this time.

*

We were working on our Maths problems when Shane leaned across.

"Hey, Peter, do you guys play football at break?" he asked.

"Yes," I told him. "Lunch-time too."

Shane nodded and said, "Great. I'll join in."

He didn't ask us.  He told us.

When the bell went, Shane followed us out into the yard.

"Let's play," he said.  "Who's got the ball?"

I showed him the ball.

"What's this?" he asked.  It was lighter than a normal football.

"The school doesn't let us have a proper football," I explained.  "In case people who aren't playing get hit by it.  We have to make do with a lighter one.  It's got something to do with health and safety.  We get a proper ball when they let us out on the big field at lunch-time – but only when it's dry."

"This is like a beach ball," Shane said, rolling it with his foot.  "It's too light.  It could go anywhere."

As if to prove his point, Shane booted it.
The ball flew over the fence and into the street,
bouncing down the pavement.

"What did you do that for?" Danny asked.
"That's why we keep the football on the ground.
Don't just launch it."

"Don't tell me what to do," Shane said.

Then they were in each other's faces, ready for a fight. I grabbed Danny's arm.

"Don't be stupid," I said. "Let's get the ball back. We're wasting time."

Their stand-off was over as soon as it had begun. Danny and I went up to the fence and got a passer-by to throw it back.

"Thanks," we said.

"Can we try to keep it on the ground this time?" I asked Shane. I added the magic word so he didn't get angry again: "Please."

Shane looked at Danny, then he looked at me. Then he grinned.

"Will do," Shane said.

He played football the same way he walked into a classroom. He was loud and he was strong. He shouted orders and knocked the other kids out of the way to get to the ball. The trouble was, Shane didn't have much control and the ball just kept running away from him. He was all energy and no skill.

"How do we tell Shane he's annoying people?" Danny said. "He's like a wild thing."

"I have an idea," I said.

I turned around and called Shane over.

"You're tall, Shane," I said. "Do you want to go in goal at lunch-time? You know, just give it a try ... for now."

Shane grinned. "Goal's good," he said.

# GOALKEEPING HISTORY

Today, everyone knows what the goalkeeper does and what they wear – but did you know things were very different in the early days of football?  Here are some of the ways the goalie's role has changed over the years.

## The first football rules didn't even mention goalkeepers

The game began to develop into what we know as football in the nineteenth century.  Back then there was no such thing as a goalkeeper – at least not in the way we think of the role today.  Instead, any player was allowed to catch the ball as long as they didn't run with it in both hands.  It wasn't until 1871 that goalkeepers were introduced into the rules and other players could no longer handle the ball.

## Keepers could handle the ball anywhere on the pitch

After the position of goalkeeper became part of the game, the rules on what they could and couldn't do kept changing.  At one point they could handle the ball anywhere on the pitch. The rule that says goalies can only handle the ball in the penalty area wasn't introduced until 1912.

## Goalkeepers haven't always worn gloves

Today, professional goalkeepers rarely play without gloves. But before the twentieth century, hardly anyone wore them. Some goalies found other things to help instead, such as Welsh player Jack Kelsey, who used to rub chewing gum between his hands to help him grip the ball! One of the first players to start wearing gloves was Argentinian Amadeo Carrizo in the 1940s.

## Goals didn't always have nets – or even a crossbar

In the nineteenth century, most football goals didn't have a net or a bar across the top of the posts. This meant the ball was often kicked high above the goalposts and created many arguments about whether or not a goal had really been scored. It wasn't until 1882 that the rules changed to say that a crossbar had to be placed across the top of the goal and the ball had to be kicked under it. Ten years later, the first net was used in an FA Cup final.

# Chapter 2
# Small goal, big keeper

Putting Shane in goal during the next game at lunch-time was the right thing to do. He took to it right away.

It was autumn, just before half-term, and it was really warm.

"It's called an Indian summer when it's warm at this time of year," Mrs Ali said.

We didn't care what it was called. The sunny weather meant the school field stayed dry, so we didn't have to play on the yard. At lunch-time we could have a full-scale match with a proper ball.  The teacher on duty acted as referee.

We learned a lot more about Shane during that game.

For starters, he would yell his head off if you gave the ball away in your own half.

"Look what you're doing," Shane barked at Danny.  "You could have given a goal away."

Ten minutes later it was my turn to get screamed at.  I tried to pass the ball upfield, but the pass was too short.  Shane had to rush out to clear the ball.  He yelled in my face at the top of his voice.

"That pass was rubbish," Shane shouted.

He tapped his head.

"Think before you play it," he told me.

"I am thinking," I said.

"Not hard enough," Shane grunted.

I glanced at Danny. It was like having
Mr Rust in goal, always giving orders.

The next thing we learned was that Shane was fast on his feet for a big guy. Hamad, who was playing for the other team, got the ball and ran straight at me. I backed off and backed off. Suddenly, Hamad moved the ball left and struck it sweetly. I spun round and saw Shane flying across the goalmouth. He tipped the ball over the crossbar with his fingertips.

"Great save!" I gasped.

Shane wasn't interested in my praise.

"Couldn't you see what Hamad was going to do?" he demanded. "You've got to stay with your man."

"Sorry," I said.

It was definitely like having Mr Rust in goal.

The third thing we learned was that Shane did things you didn't expect. Hamad got the ball again and sprinted into our penalty area. He dropped his shoulder and struck the ball with the inside of his foot. Shane was already going the wrong way to save it, but he stretched out a long leg and cleared the ball over the crossbar.

"That save was amazing," Danny said.

"It had to be amazing," Shane said, his face bright red. His eyes were hard. He roared at Danny, "You were supposed to be marking him."

"I did my best," Danny said.

"Yes, well, your best wasn't good enough," Shane snapped. "Do better!"

"Don't tell me what to do," Danny shot back. "You're not my dad."

We didn't know why then, but that comment from Danny put Shane into a rage.

"Shut your mouth!" Shane yelled. "Just shut your mouth and do your job!"

Danny was stunned. "What did you say?" he asked Shane.

"What's up?" Shane said. "Are you deaf as well as stupid?"

The teacher on duty, Mr Dunne, came over.

"Break it up, lads," he said. "It's only a game."

Shane glared at Mr Dunne, but he didn't say anything. That was the fourth thing we learned – that Shane had a temper.

"What was all that about?" Danny asked me as he jogged past.

"Beats me," I said. "He's like a bomb waiting to go off."

The bomb didn't go off that lunch-time. Shane managed to keep the lid on his temper for the rest of the game. But we did learn one last thing about him. He was a great shot stopper.

Hamad was the other team's star player. He lost his man again and burst into the penalty area. I stuck out a leg, but I timed it wrong and down went Hamad.

Penalty.

"Shane's going to have a go at me," I told Danny.

But this time Shane was too busy to shout. He strode over to Hamad and stared at him. Then he stared at the ball.

"It's a small goal," Shane said, "and I'm a big keeper."

Some of the kids laughed. Hamad frowned.

"Get back on your line, keeper," Mr Dunne told Shane.

Shane pulled a face and walked back to the goal line. Hamad stood over the ball. To put him off, Shane started wobbling his legs and waving his arms. Shane was right. He was a big keeper. Hamad did a short run-up ... and the ball flew over the bar. The kids on our team crowded round Shane.

"Did you see that?" Danny said. "Did you see how Shane psyched Hamad out?"

"Have you played in goal before?" I asked Shane.

Shane shook his head. "Never," he said.

"Well, you're playing in goal from now on," I told him. "Lots of us from school play in a Sunday League team, North Park Juniors. You should come along."

"We've already got a goalkeeper," Danny said. "Jack."

I shook my head.

"Jack hates playing in goal," I said. "Look, I'm captain and I say we give Shane a go. Jack prefers playing full-back. Well, what about it, Shane? I'll clear it with our coach."

Shane smiled.

"I don't mind if I do," he said. "Thanks, Peter."

When I got home, my dad rang Gary, our coach, to talk about Shane. Gary promised to give the new boy a chance. If Shane did well, he could be our keeper for keeps.

I rang Shane with the good news.

"Gary will need to meet your mum or dad," I told him.

"No problem," Shane said.

# GREAT GOALIES

There have been many great keepers in the history of football, and these are considered to be among the greatest of all time.

## Lev Yashin

People called Yashin the "Black Spider" or the "Black Panther" because he was so agile. He played for just one club for the whole of his career, Dynamo Moscow. He played in three World Cups and won a gold medal at the 1956 Olympics in Melbourne. Yashin saved over 150 penalty kicks and kept around 270 clean sheets.

## Gordon Banks

Gordon Banks was the goalkeeper when England won its only World Cup against West Germany in 1966. In the next World Cup in 1970, Banks faced one of the greatest players the world has ever seen, Pelé, when England played against Brazil in Mexico. Pelé headed a shot from close range, but Banks pulled off an amazing save, pushing the ball up and over the bar. Many people consider it the best save of all time.

## Iker Casillas

Casillas is one of Real Madrid's and Spain's greatest ever players. He is known as "Saint Iker" for his amazing ability to save goals. He won five Spanish league titles, three Champions League titles, six Spanish cups, two UEFA Super Cups, the FIFA Club World Cup and the Intercontinental Cup. Casillas was the captain when Spain won the European Championships in 2008 and 2012. He led Spain to World Cup glory in South Africa in 2010.

## Peter Schmeichel

Many people believe Schmeichel was Manchester United's and Denmark's greatest keeper. He played 292 times for United and won five league titles. His greatest moment was his performance in the 1999 Champions League final, when he captained the team. Schmeichel played 129 times for Denmark and helped his country win the European Championships in 1992.

# Chapter 3
# Push up!

"No problem," Shane had said when I'd told him that Gary would need to meet his mum or dad. But there was a problem and it was Shane's dad.

Shane and his dad didn't look a bit alike. Shane's dad was short and stocky with a thick neck. He had cropped hair that was going a bit grey.

"Maybe Shane is more like his mum," Danny said when I pointed this out.

But in another way, Shane was just like his dad. They were both loud.

"Right, lads," Gary said when everyone had arrived for the match on Sunday. "We've got two new lads today – Shane and Hamad. You will both be substitutes for now. I'll bring you on later." We had finally got Hamad to come along as well. After the way he played at school, he was a must for the team.

Shane's dad wasn't happy. He marched up to Gary and started talking. He didn't care that Gary was talking to another parent.

"How come our Shane isn't starting the game?" Shane's dad demanded.

Gary turned and frowned.

"Sorry," Gary said. "Do I know you?"

Shane's dad just went on talking.

"I want to know why our Shane isn't on the pitch from the beginning," he said.

He didn't even tell Gary his name.

"Oh, you're with one of the new boys," Gary said. "I've got a form for you to fill in before you go."

"You haven't answered my question," Shane's dad said, as if Gary hadn't said a word. "How come Shane isn't starting?"

"I told him," Gary said. "I will bring Shane on as a sub later. I want to see how the game goes first."

Shane's dad wasn't finished.

"I'm telling you," he said. "Our Shane is a good lad. He should be playing, not sitting on the bench."

"Well, I'm the coach," Gary said firmly. "I make the team decisions, Mr ...?"

"I'm Mick," Shane's dad said.

Mick set off down the touchline. He wasn't happy. As he passed Shane, he growled at him.

"I thought you were going to be in goal," Mick said.

For the first time ever, Shane said nothing.

"What's his dad's problem?" I asked Danny.

Danny looked at Mick and shrugged. "Beats me," he said.

The ref blew the whistle. It was an important match. We had been climbing up the table and the other team, Red Star, were in second place. If we could beat them, we would be in the top three.

The moment the match started, Mick was pacing up and down, shouting instructions even though he wasn't the coach. He marched back and forth, yelling. He got louder and louder.

"Push up! Push up!" Mick shouted.

He was yelling at us and none of the team were happy about it. Before long, Mick was waving his arms.

"Tell them, Gary," Mick said, waving his arms again. "They need to push up."

Gary shook his head. He waved at me to mark the Red Star striker alongside Danny. He was turning Danny every time. That made a difference and we started to get more of the ball. Then disaster struck. Danny lost the ball on the halfway line and Red Star had three players against one down our end. They passed the ball easily round Jack, our keeper, and rolled it in the net. Jack sighed and stared up at the sky.

Five minutes later, we were 2–0 down after a long shot that Jack fumbled and spilled in his own net. As the game resumed, Jack stayed on the goal line instead of coming out. He looked as if he was going to cry.

"Do you fancy a game?" Gary asked Shane. "Jack needs to come off.  He's lost it."

Shane glanced at Mick.

"Of course he wants a game," Mick said, speaking for Shane.  "That's why we're here."

Shane took off his jacket, pulled on his gloves and ran towards his goal without a word. It wasn't like him.  What had happened to the wild kid we knew?

He seemed to make a difference.  Shane reached every cross.  He charged out whenever Red Star attacked.  He blocked two shots – one with his hands, one with his feet.

"He's good," Gary said as I ran past him.

"Told you," Mick said, then bellowed, "Push up!"

*

Just before half-time, Gary brought Hamad on.
Red Star had another corner. Hamad started
to jog towards our goal, but Gary waved him
upfield. The Red Star winger swung the ball in
and their striker got his head to it. It looked
like a goal for sure, but Shane threw himself
across the mouth of the goal and turned the

ball round the post. He jumped up and clapped his hands. He was taking it really seriously. Shane seemed scared of failing in front of Mick.

"Come on," Shane shouted. "We're only two down. We can pull this back."

When the next corner came in, Shane grabbed the ball out of the air and barged his way past a crowd of players, knocking a couple flying. He spotted Hamad making a run and bowled the ball out. It flew half the length of the field and landed at Hamad's feet. Red Star players chased after Hamad in panic, but he was away. He dribbled the ball round the Red Star keeper and slotted it home.

Now we were only 2–1 down and the Red Star boys were looking worried.

I turned to look at Shane and he winked at me.

"We can do this," he said.

*

After half-time, the game was more even. Hamad scored a second goal to equalise and the Red Star players didn't seem so keen to come forward. Guess what Mick was shouting?

"Push up!"

Red Star spent most of the second half defending, but suddenly they broke away. Two of their players were closing in on our goal. Shane seemed in two minds. Should he come out or should he stay on his line? Finally, Shane made his choice and charged towards the boy with the ball.

It worked. Shane took the ball off the striker's foot and set off down the pitch. When he reached the halfway line, he passed the ball to the winger.

"Cross it!" Danny yelled, racing into the penalty area. "Cross it!"

The ball from the winger came in and Danny dived, meeting it with his forehead. It flew into the top corner.

"Goal!"

That's how it ended: 3–2 to North Park.

"I couldn't pick one man of the match today," Gary said afterwards, "so I've got two: you, Hamad, and you, Shane. Boys, you were both stars today."

Danny was watching Mick.

"Shane, is he always like that?" he asked.

Shane shrugged. "Pretty much," he grunted.

# DANGER! GOALKEEPER AT WORK!

Goalkeepers are often the loudest, wildest players on the pitch. There is nobody behind them to help out if they make a mistake. They are the last line of defence. If the goalkeeper fails, it costs the team a goal. That means they have to be daring and determined not to let the ball in. Here are a few wild and risky moves keepers have made to defend their goals.

## Playing through the pain

Bert Trautmann was German. He fought for his country in the Second World War and was held as a prisoner of war in England. He stayed in the country after the war and became Manchester City's goalkeeper. In the 1956 FA Cup final, Trautmann collided with another player and was knocked out. Substitutes were not allowed in 1956, so Trautmann played on despite the pain. He saved another goal and Manchester City won the match. The next day Trautmann went to the hospital. He had broken his neck, but he'd carried on playing anyway!

## A reckless tackle

Nobody can forget the 1982 World Cup semi-final between West Germany and France. French player Patrick Battiston was heading for goal when Harald Schumacher, West Germany's keeper, came charging out and crashed into Battiston. The Frenchman was left with no front teeth and a damaged back and neck.

## The scorpion kick

René Higuita was a keeper for Colombia and famous for his risky, dramatic playing style. He was always running out of his area, doing flicks, tricks and backheels. In 1995, Higuita did the impressive "scorpion kick" in a friendly against England at Wembley. It was a kind of somersault, clearing the ball with his heels.

# Chapter 4
# Flattened

Shane was in a really bad mood the next morning at school. Nobody knew why. When the first bell went, Shane stamped across the classroom to his seat, dropped into it and sat with his arms folded. His eyes blazed.

"What's the matter with Shane?" Danny asked. "He looks ready for a fight."

He wasn't wrong.

"Shane," Mrs Ali said, "would you give the books out, please?"

Shane didn't say a word, and he didn't move.

"Shane," Mrs Ali repeated, "would you give the books out, please?"

Still nothing from Shane. Mrs Ali tried again.

"Shane," she began. "Would you—"

"Fine," Shane said. He got up suddenly and his chair fell on the floor. "I'll give the stupid books out."

Shane marched up and down, slapping the books on the desks. As soon as he had finished, he went back to his seat and stayed there, staring at the floor.

At break-time Shane was following us outside when Mrs Ali called him back.

"Shane," she said, "is everything OK?"

Danny glanced at me, then we went outside without a word. Shane joined us in the yard five minutes later.

"Are you all right?" I asked.

"Why does everybody keep asking me that?" Shane snapped. "I'm fine."

But Shane didn't look fine. He didn't act fine. He was the same back in class. Mrs Ali asked him things, but he only gave one-word answers.

It got worse at lunch-time. Shane sat on his own to eat his packed lunch. He didn't want to talk to anyone. But he did agree to play football.

It was a bad mistake. Shane charged this way and that. He came off his line for balls he couldn't reach. He fell on people. He was like a whirlwind. Danny had some advice.

"Just calm down, will you, Shane?" he said.

Shane touched his nose with his finger. "Keep your nose out of my business," he said.

Danny turned towards me. "Touchy," he said.

That set Shane off. "What did you say?"

"I said," Danny answered, "that you are being a bit touchy."

Before I knew it, Shane was throwing punches and had knocked Danny to the ground.

Mrs Ali was on duty. She came running over and stood between Danny and Shane.

"What is wrong with you?" Danny cried, jumping to his feet.

"Nothing's wrong with me," Shane yelled. "What's wrong with you?"

Mrs Ali made the time-out sign with her hands.

"OK, guys," she said, "let's go over there and have a word."

It was a long word. The rest of us tried to get on with the game, but no one's heart was in it. We were glad when the bell went.

"Do you know why Shane is so wound up?" I asked Danny back in class.

"I think something's going on at home," Danny said. "When Mrs Ali asked Shane about it, he started to get angry again."

\*

Soon it was Sunday again and Shane was still angry. He saw me looking at him before our North Park match started.

"Don't ask me if I'm all right," Shane said. "Just don't."

We were playing Five Ways, a team down at the bottom of the league. They didn't look very confident.

"They should be a pushover," Mick said.

Gary frowned. Some of the parents of the Five Ways boys were listening.

"Mick," Gary said, "can you keep it down, please? I always tell the team to show respect."

Mick nodded, but five minutes later he was back to normal, yelling at us from the sidelines.

"Push up!" Mick shouted. "Come on, boys. Push up!"

Then Five Ways were on the attack.

"Mark him," Mick yelled. "Mark that lad on the wing, Peter. Mark him!"

I went out to the winger, but who made Mick the coach? He was getting on my nerves.

The winger whipped the ball into the penalty area before I could reach him. Shane rushed across to punch it clear ... and nearly took the striker's head off. The boy went down in a heap. Everybody ran to stand round him. On the touchline, Mick was giving his point of view.

"Shane hardly touched him," he said. "Oh, come on. Get up, lad. Football isn't a game for wimps."

Some of the Five Ways parents were glaring at Mick. The ref gave Shane a warning and eventually the striker got up and we played on.

We had a corner and Danny scored with a header. Shane was yelling and punching the air. Mick ran onto the pitch, slapping us all on the back.

"That's more like it, boys," he said.

Danny looked at me and shook his head.
"What a muppet," he said.

"Go back to the touchline, please," the ref
told Mick.

Then Hamad scored just before half-time
and we came off the pitch 2–0 up.

"Have you seen Shane's face?" Danny asked.
"He looks as if we're 2–0 down."

It was true.  Shane sat apart from us ... and
from Mick.  What *was* going on?

\*

Halfway through the second half, Five Ways
got a corner.  Shane was jumping up and down
on his line, commanding his area.  As the ball
came in, the Five Ways centre-half went for the
ball.  Shane had the same idea ... They came

together and there was only one winner. Shane caught the ball – and flattened the boy. He took a long time to get up.

"That's it," the ref said.

"What?" Shane said. "What did I do?"

Mick joined in. "Come off it, ref," he said. "That wasn't even a foul."

The ref called Gary over and said, "Take him off, coach, before I send him off."

Gary nodded.

"Do us all a favour, Mick," Gary said. "Take Shane home and let him cool off. I'll give you a ring later."

"You're having a laugh," Mick said. "What did Shane do wrong? It isn't a game for—"

"Wimps," Gary sighed. "You've said that before.  Look, Mick, the other boy could have been badly hurt this time."

"Then he should toughen up," Mick said.

Gary shook his head.  "Mick," he said, "I am not discussing it here.  I will call you later."  He turned to Shane.  "You go with your dad."

Shane marched off across the field towards the car park.

"Fine," Shane said.  "I'm going."  Then he pointed at Mick.  "But he isn't my dad."

# GOALKEEPING HOWLERS

Even the best goalkeepers have bad days. And when the goalie makes a mistake, it all goes wrong for the whole team. Here are a few goalie howlers.

## A lucky streak before disaster strikes

Italian keeper Massimo Taibi joined Manchester United in 1999, replacing the legendary Peter Schmeichel. He was man of the match in two games. Then disaster struck when Southampton's Matt Le Tissier hit a gentle shot in the next game. The ball dribbled through Taibi's hands and ended up in the back of the net. Taibi only played once more for United in a 5–0 defeat at Chelsea.

## Careless hands

Gary Sprake played in a very good side, Don Revie's Leeds United. They won a lot of trophies. The team didn't give goals away easily, but Sprake made some terrible howlers. The most famous came in 1967, when Sprake threw the ball into his own net in front of the Kop at Liverpool's Anfield ground. The

Liverpool fans sang the pop song "Careless Hands" in the second half!

## Messing up when it matters most

Liverpool keeper Bruce Grobbelaar made some howlers in the biggest club competition of them all: the European Cup. The first disaster was against CSKA Sofia in the 1982 quarter-final. Grobbelaar rushed out of his goal to catch a cross, missed, and Mladenov headed the ball into an empty net. A year later Liverpool were playing the Polish team Widzew Lodz when Grobbelaar tried to catch a cross with one hand and missed again. It cost Liverpool a goal.

## Two fatal errors

David Seaman played in goal for Arsenal and England. He was a good keeper, but that didn't stop him having bad days. In the 1995 Cup Winners' Cup final, Nayim of Real Zaragoza kicked the ball into Seaman's goal from the halfway line, winning the match in the final minute. This mistake was topped in the 2002 World Cup when Ronaldinho of Brazil had a free kick and it flew over Seaman's hands. England lost the match.

# Chapter 5
# The best

The next day in school, there was no sign of Shane.

"Do you think Shane's all right?" I said to Danny. "After what happened at the match, I'm worried about him."

"Why don't you call round his house after school?" Danny said. "It's on the way home."

"Why me?" I asked.

"You're his mate," Danny said.

"So are you," I said.

"OK," Danny said. "We'll both go."

We looked at each other. Danny had said I was Shane's mate. Was I? We played football in the same team, but what did I know about him? He was a mystery – a big, angry mystery.

"What do we know about Shane?" I asked.

"He's loud," Danny said.

I nodded. "True."

"He's from Leeds."

"Yes," I said. It was my turn. "He's a great keeper."

Danny nodded. "He's got a rotten temper."

I sighed. "And Mick isn't his dad."

"He might be," Danny said.

"What do you mean?" I asked. "Shane said he wasn't. Why would he lie?"

"Haven't you ever said it?" Danny said. "You get angry and you say: 'You're not my real dad.'"

I thought about it for a minute. "No, not really," I replied. "I've never said that."

Danny grinned. "No, me neither, but I can imagine Shane saying it."

\*

After school, we called on Shane. While we were standing outside the house, Danny was the first to say, "Ask Shane about his dad."

"No chance," I said. "You ask him. Anyway, he says Mick isn't his dad."

"Why do I have to do it?" Danny asked.

We looked across the road at Shane's house. There was a board taped over the window where somebody had smashed the glass.

Then Danny pointed and said, "Talk of the devil."

Shane must have seen us, as he came out of the house, shutting the door behind him. He checked the road for cars and crossed over.

"What are you doing here?" Shane asked.

I was the first to answer. "You weren't in school today, Shane. You don't look sick to me. What's up?"

Shane took a moment to answer. "OK," he said, "it's like this. Mick shouted at me all the way home yesterday after the match. He said I was an idiot, getting sent off like that."

"You didn't get sent off," I said. "The ref asked Gary to take you off for your own good."

"Same thing, according to Mick," Shane said. "He said I let him down."

"That's daft," I said. "It isn't about Mick. He was only watching."

Danny pointed at the broken window and the board. "Did Mick do that?" he asked.

Shane nodded. "He was in a rage," he said. "He smashed the window. Mum put the board up."

"Why did you say Mick's not your dad?" Danny asked. "I mean, you don't have to tell us."

"But we want to know," I added. (I have always been nosy.)

"There's no point keeping it a secret," Shane said. "My dad left years ago. I don't know where he is now. He never gets in touch. My mum started going out with Mick last year. It was the wrong move. Mick's bad news. He causes trouble everywhere he goes."

"Bad news how?" I asked.

Shane shrugged. "You've seen the way Mick is at football. Just imagine what he's like at home. He's scary. I was watching TV once and he stamped on the remote control and broke it."

Danny gave Shane a sideways look. "You can be pretty scary yourself," he said.

"Really?" Shane asked.

"Really."

After that, we all laughed.

"So why did Mick smash the window?" Danny asked.

Shane closed his eyes, as if he was reliving it. "When we got home, Mick was still yelling at me. He pushed me into the house and told me to go to my room."

"Did you go?" I asked.

"No way," Shane said. "Who's Mick to tell me what to do?"

"Because he isn't your dad," Danny said.

Shane clapped his hands together. "Exactly. Anyway, he tried to make me go upstairs and I wouldn't do it."

I leaned forward. "What happened next?" I asked.

"My mum stuck up for me," Shane said. "That made Mick even angrier. He always wants to be the boss. What he says goes. Mum said I was her son, not his. I stuck up for her. Then Mick threw a chair at the window."

"He never!" I said.

Shane nodded. "He did. The police came and took him away."

Danny whistled.

"Weren't you scared?" I asked.

"Of course," Shane said, "but I've got to stick up for my mum."

I looked at Danny. Was Shane crying? I squeezed his arm.

"Gary says you can play on Sunday," I said.

Shane rubbed his eyes with his sleeve. "You're kidding?" he said.

I told him it was true. "Cross my heart," I said.

Shane still couldn't believe it. "I thought I was finished with North Park," he said. "I made a fool of myself yesterday."

Danny butted in. "You're the best keeper we've ever had," he said.

Shane blew his nose. "How many keepers have you had?" he asked.

Danny thought. "Well, just Jack, but you're still the best. Jack's a good full-back but a rubbish keeper. He flaps at crosses."

"You're the best, Shane," I agreed. "You make the team solid at the back."

"So, who are we playing next?" Shane asked, his face lighting up.

"It's the big one," Danny said. "We're playing Delta Boys. It's first against second in the league. If we win, we go top instead of them.

I know it's early in the season, but it would be a good place to be."

"And Gary trusts me to be in goal after yesterday?" Shane asked.

"Yes, Gary said he'll give you another chance," I said.

"But for how long?" Shane said. "What if I mess up again?"

"That's down to you, isn't it?" Danny said. "No one can control your temper but you."

Shane nudged him in the ribs and said, "That's deep, that is."

"Not really," I said. "Danny doesn't do deep."

Danny was laughing. "What a cheek!" he said.

But it was true.

# GOALIES' GOALS

Have you ever seen the keeper racing down the field to try to score at the other end? It normally happens near the end of matches when there is nothing to lose. Some keepers love to have a go at being the striker.

## Spotting an opportunity

In 1996, José Luis Chilavert was playing for Velez Sarsfield against River Plate. He said he saw the other goalie watching birds instead of the game, so Chilavert kicked the ball 60 metres into the opposition net. Chilavert has an amazing record of goals for a keeper – he scored 59 club goals and 8 goals for his national team.

## The winning goal

On the last day of the 1998–99 season, Carlisle needed a win against Plymouth to stay in the Football League. With ten seconds to go, they were drawing 1–1. It looked like the end of Carlisle's time in the League. But then their keeper Jimmy Glass went to help his team with a late corner. The ball came out to him and Glass volleyed it home. Fans poured onto the pitch. Carlisle stayed in the League thanks to Glass.

## A last-minute save

Oscarine Masuluke scored a fantastic goal in the South African Premier League against Orlando Pirates in 2016. His team, Baroka, were losing, and Masuluke went up for a last-minute corner. The ball spun into the air at the edge of the penalty area. Masuluke threw himself upwards and did a brilliant overhead kick. The ball flew into the top corner of the net, and his team drew the match.

## Scoring from the halfway line!

Egyptian keeper Essam El Hadary was playing in the 2002 CAF Super Cup, with his Al Ahly side 2–1 up over Kaizer Chiefs. Al Ahly got a free kick close to the halfway line and El Hadary saw that the other keeper, Brian Baloyi, was off his line. He hit the ball over Baloyi's head and into the net.

# Chapter 6
## Keeper for keeps

Mick wasn't on the touchline the next Sunday morning.  Shane's mum was there instead.

"Where did the police take Mick?" I asked.

"I don't know," Shane said, "and I don't care.  His stuff's gone from our house.  Good riddance!"

Shane pulled on his goalie gloves.  His hands looked like spades in them.

"So this is the big one?" he said.

"Yes," I told him. "We played Delta in the first game of the season. They hammered us 5–0."

Danny chuckled. "Yes, but we had Jack in goal," he said, "so it doesn't count."

Jack was nearby. "Hey, I heard that," he said.

"Yes, but you really are rubbish in goal," Danny said.

Jack nodded. "It's funny because it's true."

He jogged into the full-back position. Danny and I took our places in midfield. It was the first cold day of the autumn. We were in our long-sleeved shirts and we were still freezing. The wind was howling across the pitch and there was rain in the air.

"Come on, ref," Hamad said. "Blow the whistle."

"Be careful what you wish for," I told him. "Delta battered us last time we met."

It soon looked like it was going to go the same way this time. The Delta players swept forward in numbers. They tried two long shots from outside the penalty area. Shane caught the first shot, but the second one stung his hands and rebounded. Shane had to throw himself to the ground to grab the follow-up shot. The nearest Delta player tapped Shane's head with his boot when the ref wasn't looking.

"See that, ref?" Danny cried.

The ref hadn't seen it. I expected Shane to start yelling, but he just got to his feet and rolled the ball out to Hamad.

Shane glanced at his mum. She smiled and gave the thumbs up. He was a different player when Mick wasn't there and nobody was telling us to push up.

Delta were still on the attack. Their striker burst into the penalty area, but Shane pounced on the ball before he could shoot. This time Shane got a knee in the face and the ref saw it. He sent the Delta striker off. I stared at Shane.

"What's got into you?" I said. "You didn't even get angry with that player."

Shane shrugged. "Let's get on with the game, eh?" he said.

Even with ten men, the Delta midfield didn't give us a moment to breathe. They snapped into tackles. They got so close you could feel their breath on your neck.

Danny was making mistakes. So was I. I tried to turn with the ball and ended up putting it in the path of their winger. He left me stranded on the floor and raced towards the goal. Danny charged in to stop him and mishit the ball, sending it flying towards our goal. I groaned. It was going to be an own goal. The winger was already running away to celebrate.

But he hadn't counted on Shane. For a big guy, he was as quick as lightning. Shane had to jump to his right and twist backwards at the same time. But he did it. He pushed the ball wide with his fingertips.

The winger stared. He couldn't believe his eyes. The ball was in play, so he chased it and sent it back across the goalmouth. Shane reached out and palmed the ball over the bar. I went to pat Shane on the back, but he shoved me away. He tapped his head.

"Stay alert," he yelled.

This was more like the old Shane, bossing his box.

"Danny, mark your man," he added.

The ball from the corner looped over my head, but Shane grabbed it, hugging it to his belly. He spotted Hamad and bowled it downfield.

Now the Delta players were caught at the wrong end of the pitch. Hamad took the ball on his chest, raced into the box and hit it with the top of his boot. It flew into the roof of the Delta net.

One attack.

1–0 up.

"Goal!" Shane yelled, dancing on his line and punching the air with his fists. "Keep it tight," he shouted. "Five minutes to half-time."

Delta were still coming forward and we were defending deep.

"Push up!" Shane yelled. He sounded just like Mick.

We all looked at him and burst out laughing.

"OK," Shane said, "you've had your fun. Keep your eyes on the ball."

Delta had one more attack before half-time. Their shot took a deflection and Shane had to shift his weight. He just managed to get a hand to the ball, pushing it onto the post and out of play. The whistle went for half-time.

"Well, I have never seen a team get such a hammering and come in 1–0 up," Gary said in his team talk. "Try to squeeze the play a bit in the second half."

Danny nudged me, whispering, "He means push up."

The second half started the same way as the first. Even with ten against eleven, the Delta forwards were all over us and we had every player in defence except Hamad. Shane was amazing, plucking the ball out of the air, pushing it onto the crossbar, gathering it at his feet. The Delta captain shook his head.

"If it wasn't for your keeper," he said, "you'd be 5–0 down."

It was true, but even the best keeper can't do it all. Something had to give. The Delta striker hit the ball from the edge of the penalty area. He scuffed it, but the ball hit me on the ankle and Shane was going the wrong way, unable to change his footing in time.

1–1.

Delta pushed forward, wanting the winner, but Shane was at the top of his game. Nothing got past him. He roared and shouted. He waved and pointed. I don't know if we did anything he said, but it showed Shane was the boss. I even forgot I was the captain.

But that wasn't the end. Hamad came back to defend a corner and threw out his arm to stop a shot.

"Hand ball!" yelled the Delta captain.

The ref gave them a penalty. I thought Shane was going to yell at Hamad, but he didn't say a word. Shane put on a show instead. He did a weird dance in front of the Delta penalty-taker.

"Get on your line, keeper," the ref said.

Shane tilted his head. Then he moonwalked to the line. Everybody laughed. The Delta captain stood over the ball.

"Keeper, knock off the play-acting," the ref warned again.

Shane gave an army salute. "Yes, sir."

The Delta captain sighed and did his run-up. The ball flew over the bar and the Delta captain sank to his knees, holding his head. Shane's tricks had worked. He put the ball down for a goal kick and spotted Hamad moving away from his marker.

"Hamad," Shane yelled. "Go left!"

The Delta centre-half saw the danger too late. Finally, having eleven players against ten was making a difference. Nobody was marking Hamad and he was away. The long ball from Shane floated towards Hamad, who got his head to it.

"Goal!" Shane shouted.

After that, Delta ran out of steam. We were 2–1 winners.

"Top of the table, lads," Danny said.

"Thanks to Shane," I reminded him.

"So do I get to keep my place between the posts?" Shane asked.

"Of course," Gary said. "You're our keeper for keeps."

Our books are tested
for children and young people by
children and young people.

Thanks to everyone who consulted on
a manuscript for their time and effort in
helping us to make our books better
for our readers.